I Drw By
♡ ELVEn

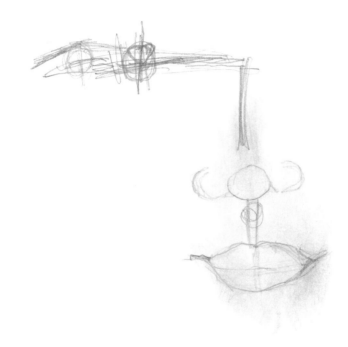

better together*

*This book is best read together, grownup and kid.

■ akidsbookabout.com

this book colored
by

a kids book about™

emotions

color me!

by Nakita Simpson

a
kids
book
about™

Printed in the United States of America

Library of Congress cataloging available.

A Kids Book About books are exclusively available online
on the A Kids Book About website.

To share your stories, ask questions, or inquire about bulk
purchases (schools, libraries, and nonprofits), please use
the following email address:

hello@akidsbookabout.com

www.akidsbookabout.com

ISBN: 978-1-951253-39-4

To my mom, who's done everything she can
to make sure I always have a safe space
in this world with her.

Intro

The most powerful way people make connections today is through our emotions—by seeing them in others and ourselves. When we're little, emotions can feel like a lot to process, so it doesn't hurt to have some practice in expressing them so we can learn how to navigate them in the future.

Emotions change and grow over the years, and so does our understanding of them! So this book is just as helpful for kids as it is for grownups, which is why the activities are made for everyone reading. There's no wrong way to color or write how we feel inside (or outside) this coloring book, so don't be afraid to get messy.

I wrote this book as a tool to help grownups and kids talk about their emotions, what they mean, and how to express them in a healthy and safe way. So color, write, doodle, and express how you feel and explore your wonderful range of emotions!

i wonder
what you're
feeling
today. . .

If I asked you to describe your emotions, could you?

Honestly, sometimes I don't even know what *I'm* feeling.

Sometimes
I feel so **happy**
that my cheeks hurt...

Like I might

from excitement!

Other days
I feel
a little
hopeless

and

sad

and I can't wait
for the day to end.

But most days,
I have so many emotions
I can't even count them.

And they don't just come
one at a time,
but all at once!

Have you ever felt

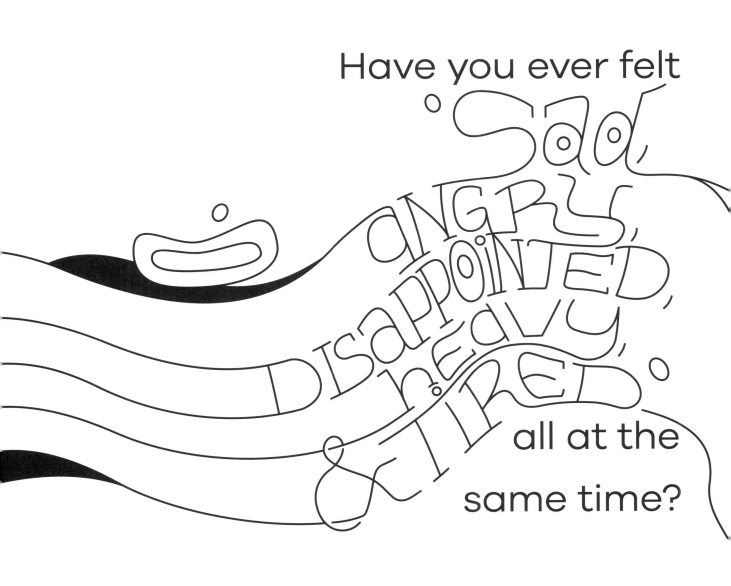

all at the

same time?

Sometimes I don't know how to talk about my feelings, but I can usually draw them.

So I made this a coloring book!
**Let's see if you can describe
your emotions now....**

....But with a drawing.

Draw how you feel here.
Feel free to use any and all colors
to express how you're feeling.

draw
here

-(draw anywhere)-

What even are **emotions**?

Are they things we feel?

Things that we make happen?

Or things that happen to us?

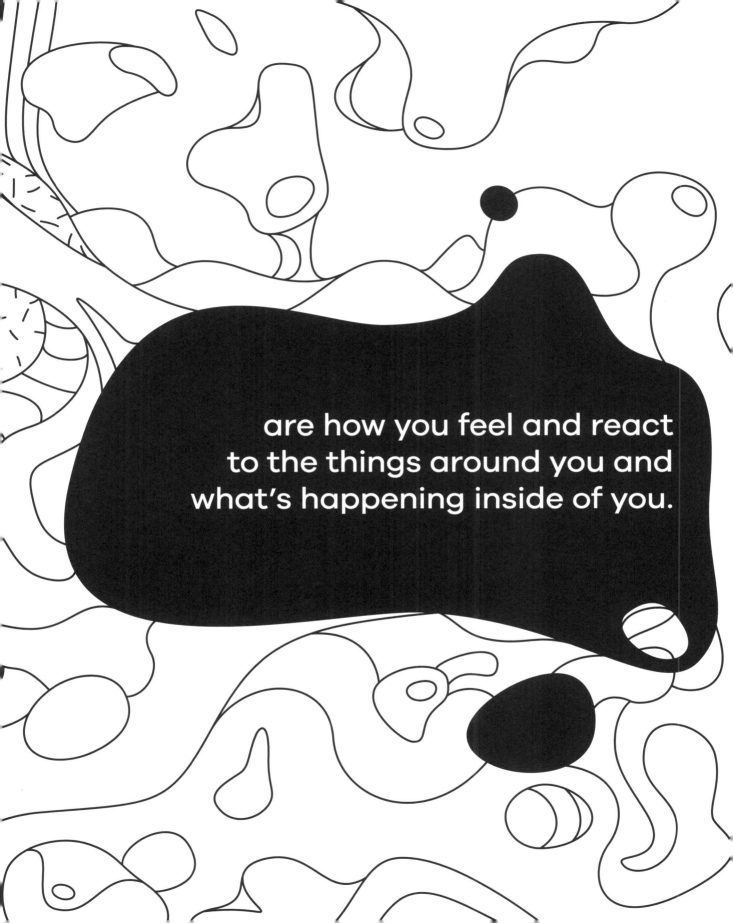

are how you feel and react
to the things around you and
what's happening inside of you.

This can be when someone is nice to you and it makes you feel **happy**.

Or when someone hurts you and you feel **pain** or **sadness**.

It can even be when someone gives you a gift, and you feel **nervous** or **guilty**.

That's weird right?

There are times that you can have certain emotions, but not know why.

Nothing happened,
but for some reason,
you're **jealous**, or **scared**,
or **feel like crying**.

Emotions

are complicated.

Write down some emotions you've felt today:

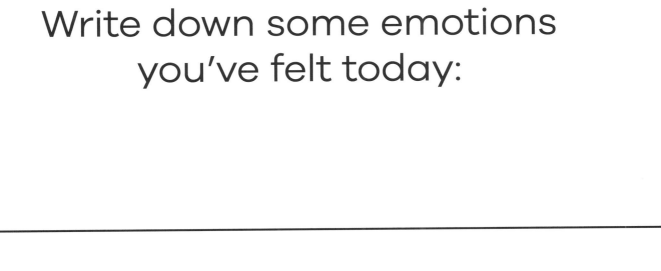

If you were in a room surrounded by people, **how would you feel?**

Some kids get **elated*** when they're in a crowd of people.

***Elated** means really happy.*

But other kids in the same situation can feel **anxious** and **overwhelmed**.

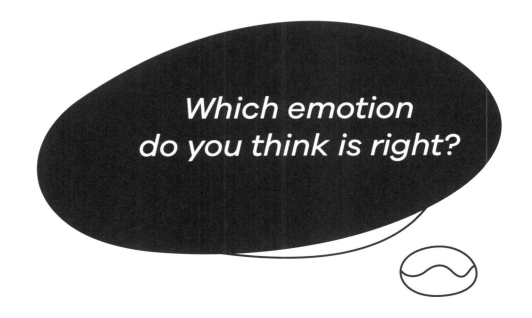

Which emotion do you think is right?

ALL OF THEM ARE RIGHT!

There is no *right* or *wrong* way to feel.

Everyone feels differently.

What matters is how we **act** with our emotions.

What are you and your grownup feeling while you read this book?

Can you name some of those feelings now?

kid

---

grownup

Emotions aren't just complicated,
a lot of times,
they can be **scary**.

They don't always feel
like sunny days.

They can be really hard.

Like when your parents yell at each other.

Or when a parent leaves.

When your friends leave you out.

Or you move and don't have any friends.

When you get a bad grade and your grownup is disappointed in you.

And then there's...

bullying,

getting made fun of,

not liking yourself,

not fitting in, feeling misunderstood, feeling guilty, feeling lost.

Sometimes when I have these kinds of emotions, I try to pretend like they don't exist.

I bury them deep down,
so they can't come out.

And when someone asks how I'm feeling, I say things like...

or

And after a while
I might even convince myself
that I am fine
or OK...

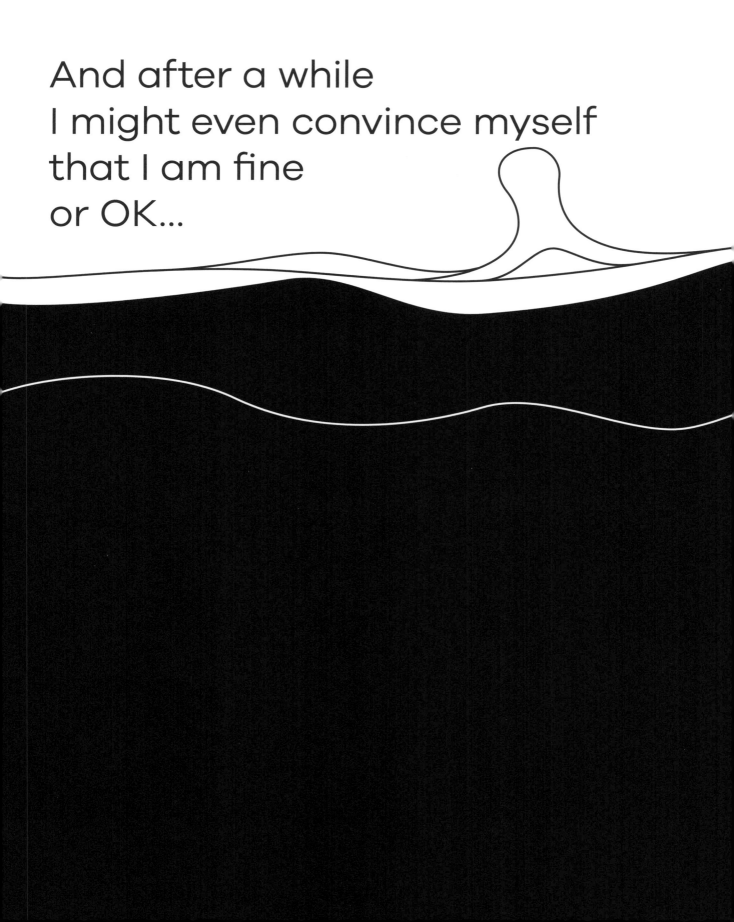

But the truth is,
I'm not sure how to
explain what I'm feeling
or what to do about it.

So I keep all my emotions
bottled up inside me until
they all come out in

unexpected ways

like yelling

or getting angry

and I end up hurting
the people around me.

Sometimes,
I end up even hurting myself.

It's like a

emotion MONSTER.

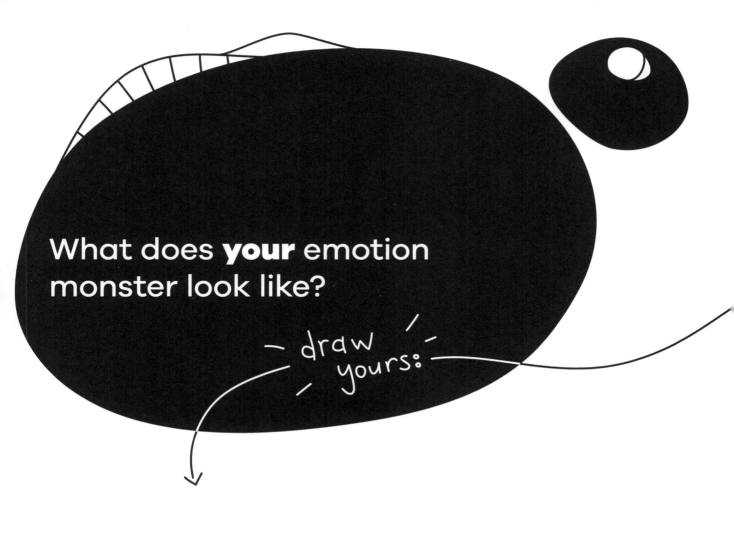

What does **your** emotion monster look like?

- draw yours:

We shouldn't be
scared of our emotions!

(Or our emotion monsters.)

I'll tell you a secret...

If you get really good at what I'm about to tell you next, you'll be better at this than most grownups.

But first,
know that it's **OK to feel.**

That comes before anything else.

Give yourself permission
to have emotions.

To feel.

And once you've given yourself
the right to do that—

here comes the secret........

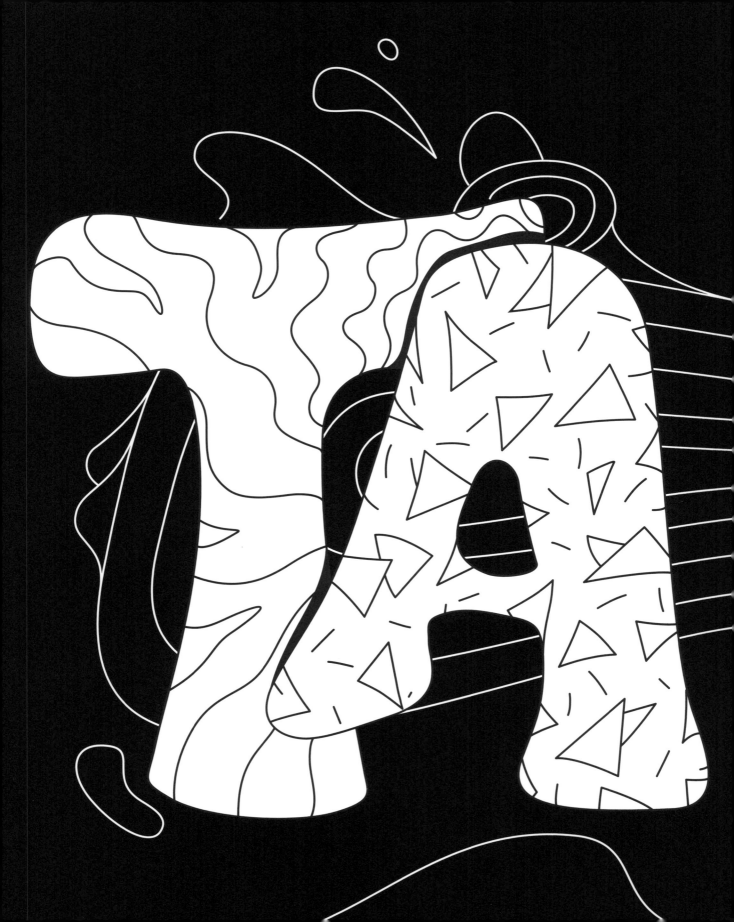

Talk about your emotions.

It might seem easy
and like anybody could do it,
but it's not.

It can be really hard.

It can be **uncomfortable**, **scary**, and make you feel **vulnerable**.*

*_**Vulnerable** means putting yourself out there and being open to whatever can happen._

But when you talk about your emotions something incredible happens...

You can understand them.

And when you understand your emotions, they don't feel so scary anymore and you can become friends with your emotion monster!

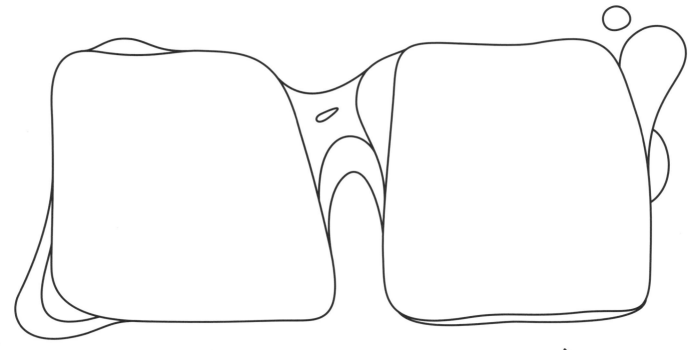

Don't believe me? Try it!

Find someone safe that you trust, either a grownup or a friend, and talk to them.

Put down words, or pictures, or anything that describes how you're feeling and don't worry about whether it "makes

draw your own!

color this in with the color that best suits how you're feeling

And don't stop there!

Ask other people how they're feeling and keep talking.

Be a safe person for them to share **their** emotions with.

And if they don't want to share, that's OK too.

It's up to them.

Remember, emotions are complicated and weird sometimes...

...but we all feel them.
And talking about it can help
make them less confusing.

For kids **and** grownups.

— the —
end

but there's
more

Need help finding the right word for how you feel?

TRY THIS:

calm
tired
sleepy
underwhelmed
SAD
depressed
hurt
guilty
lonely
vulnerable
SCARED
fearful
anxious
insecure
shame
weak
overwhelmed
awkward
shy
nervous
EXCITED
ecstatic
silly
energetic
shocked
anxious

often happy

curious
tense
UPSET
horrified
disgusted ←
annoyed
disappointed
— grief
awful
guilty
contemptuous
ANGRY
furious
mad ←
hateful
bitter
irritated
frustrated
conflicted
HAPPY
elated
joyful
appreciated
proud
— brave
ambivalent

+ sad ←

but
also
fearful ←

write your own:

Outro

Now you have a couple of handy words and exercises for your kids to help them share what's going on inside their hearts and minds. So be sure to put them into practice the next time anyone is struggling to understand their emotions—kid, grownup, or otherwise.

Talk it out, draw it out, paint or color it out, and invite them into the process of expression. There's no one way to talk about our emotions. All roads lead to feeling heard, understood, loved, and seen!

find more kids books about

optimism, empathy, death,
anxiety, failure, gratitude,
depression, voting,
bullying, god,
and change.

■ akidsbookabout.com

share your read*

*Tell somebody, post a photo, or give this book away to share what you care about.

@akidsbookabout